Who's New in Our School?

written by Anne Lawrence
illustrated by Cynthia McGrellis

**McGraw-Hill
School Division**

New York   Farmington

Today I am talking with a new boy in
our school. He is in the second grade.
His name is Luis Pablo Galis.

Tom: Luis Pablo, where are you from?

Luis Pablo: I am from Santo Domingo.
It is in the Dominican Republic.

Tom: Where is that?

Luis Pablo: The Dominican Republic is in the Caribbean Sea.

Tom: Luis Pablo, your English is very good. Did you learn it in school?

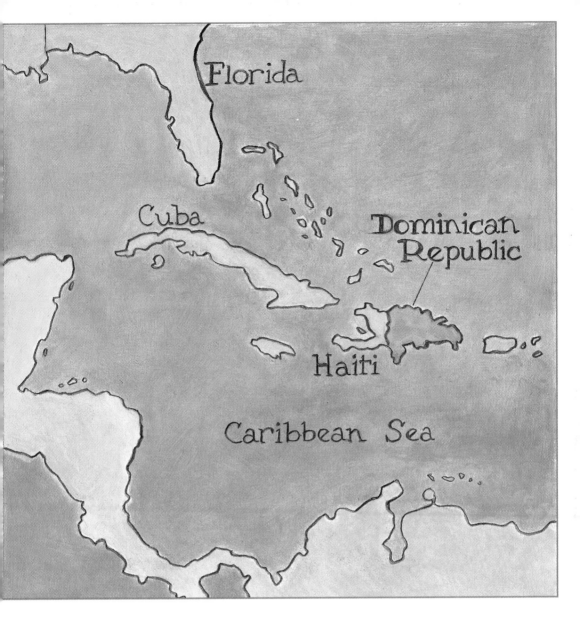

Luis Pablo: No. I'm lucky. I learned it from my mother. She was born here in Florida. My mother always speaks English with my two sisters and me. With my father, we always speak Spanish. So we know both.

Tom: What a great way to learn!

Luis Pablo: Yes. It is fun, too.

Tom: Why did your family move to Florida?

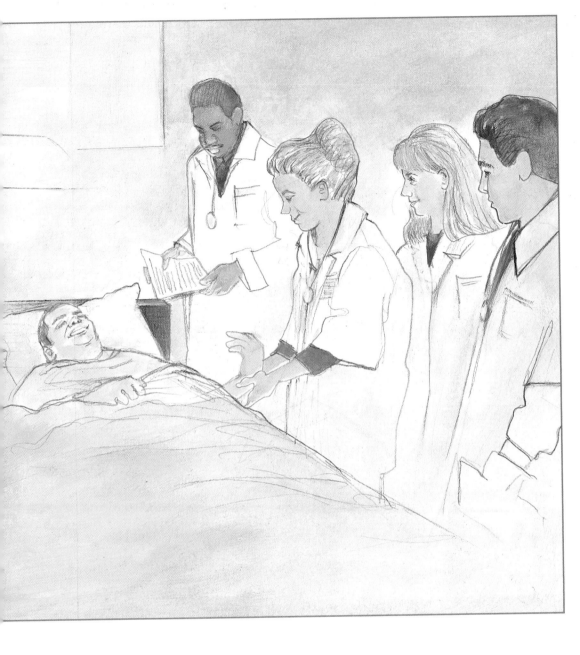

Luis Pablo: My mother got a job at a book company here.

Tom: And your father?

Luis Pablo: He is studying to be a doctor. He is starting at a new school, too.

Tom: What do you miss about your old home?

Luis Pablo: I miss Ella. That is my name for my mother's mother. I love her so much. I miss her cooking, too.

Tom: What is her best dish?

Luis Pablo: I love her yellow rice, with carrots and peppers.

Tom: That sounds good! Now, you talked about your sisters. How old are they?

Luis Pablo: One is a baby. She crawls all over the place. The other is six. She is in first grade.

Tom: What do kids do for fun in Santo Domingo?

Luis Pablo: We do what American kids do. We play games. We watch TV. We read. All around Santo Domingo is the sea. So we go there a lot.

Tom: To swim?

Luis Pablo: Yes, and to fish. I can catch a lot of fish!

Tom: We fish here in Florida, too.

Luis Pablo: That's great!

Tom: What other things do you like to do?

Luis Pablo: I love to listen to music and dance!

Tom: Dance?

Luis Pablo: Yes. All the people back home love to dance!

Tom: What if you are shy?

Luis Pablo: You can't be shy when you are dancing.

Tom: Did you get a lot of homework back home?

Luis Pablo: Yes. I hope I won't have as much here.

Tom: I'm sure you will!

Luis Pablo: Oh, well. It will be the same, then.

Tom: Do you play soccer?

Luis Pablo: No, I like baseball much better.

15

Tom: What position do you play?

Luis Pablo: I'm the shortstop. I'm very good at it. Every day, I hurry to the ball park to play.

Tom: After you finish your homework, right?

Luis Pablo: Sí, after my homework!